# TAD LINCOLN:
## White House Wildcat

Written by
**David R. Collins**

Illustrated by
**Leslie Carow Ossoff**

**Discovery Enterprises, Ltd.**
**Lowell, Massachusetts**
**1995**

ISBN 1-878668-33-1 hard cover / library edition; 1-878668-40-4 paperback

Library of Congress Catalog Card Number 94-71900

10 9 8 7 6 5 4 3 2 1

*Printed in the United States of America*

**Subject Reference Guide:**

Collins, David R.
*Tad Lincoln: White House Wildcat*
Illustrated by Leslie Carow Ossoff

1. Lincoln, Thomas (Tad) - Juvenile Literature
2. Lincoln, Abraham - Juvenile Literature
3. White House - Juvenile Literature

# *Table of Contents*

# Dedication

*This book is for my nephew, Ryan,*
*who like Tad Lincoln lost his father far too early,*
*yet still managed to bring my brother so much pride*
*and happiness during their short time together.*

# Chapter One

The boy slipped inside the big door.
He looked both ways and listened.
There was no one in sight.
He could not hear a sound.

He looked down at his hands and arms.
They were covered with strawberry juice.
Slowly the boy tiptoed toward the main staircase.
Again he stopped and listened.
Still there was no sound.

Smiling, he darted up the steps.
He had almost reached the top when —

"Tad! I want to talk with you."

The boy turned to face his father.
The tall man stood at the bottom of the staircase.

"The gardener came to see me today."
The man paused, rubbing his long chin.
"It seems something has been eating our strawberries.
The gardener said it must be that wildcat again."

Eight-year-old Tad Lincoln came down the steps.
His head was drooping.
"It's the gardener's fault," the boy said.
"He should not grow strawberries so fresh and juicy."

Abraham Lincoln looked at his son.
"So that is the problem.
Thank you, Tad.
I shall tell the gardener that.
From now on he must grow the strawberries old and dry."

The tall man turned to go.
''Wait —'' Tad said.
''That is foolish.''

Abraham Lincoln nodded.
''Yes, it is.
I shall simply let the man go.
He can find work some other place.''
Again the tall man turned away.

''No, Pa, you can't do that!''
Tad Lincoln shook his head.
''I have the answer.''

''Good,'' Abraham Lincoln said.
''Please share it with me.''

Tad smiled.

"I shall catch the wildcat myself.
I will make the wildcat do what I say.
I promise you the strawberries will be safe
from now on."

"That is a fine promise," the older man said.
"You can tell the gardener of it.
The news is sure to please him."

Tad turned and started up the steps again.

“Oh. . .and Tad?”
“Yes, Pa?”

“Since the wildcat will not be eating our strawberries. . .”
Abraham Lincoln stopped.

“Yes, Pa?”

“Maybe he can help you clean your room.
He will have more time for such things.
Now that he will not be eating our strawberries.”

Tad nodded.
“Yes, Pa.”
Quickly the boy hurried off to bed.

# *Chapter Two*

"White House Wildcat" was just one of
Tad Lincoln's nicknames.
He was born in 1853 in Springfield, Illinois.
His real name was Thomas.
But he wiggled like a tadpole.
So his father nicknamed him Tad.

Abraham Lincoln was a lawyer in Springfield.
He wore a long black coat and a tall black hat.
Sometimes he kept his lawyer papers in his hat.
Mrs. Lincoln just shook her head when he did.
But Tad did not care.

Little Tad shook the papers out.
Then he put the tall hat on.
No one could see his head.
"Who took my son's head?" Abraham Lincoln asked.
Tad laughed and pulled the hat off.

"Here I am, Pa!" Tad squealed.
His father would pick him up and whirl him around.
Tad liked Pa's rides.

Tad liked Pa to pull him in his wagon.
Tad's brother Willie liked to ride too.
One morning Abraham Lincoln piled both boys in the wagon.
They headed down the street.

People stopped to talk with Abraham Lincoln.
They got him thinking about lots of things.
He sometimes forgot what he was doing.

On this morning he forgot about Tad and Willie.
He just pulled the wagon and thought about other things.
Suddenly the wagon hit a bump.
Plop!
Out popped Tad on the ground.

His father just kept walking.

Willie giggled.

He giggled louder when Tad yelled.

Big brothers are like that sometimes.

Finally, Abraham Lincoln came to the end of the street.

He turned around.

There sat Willie, still giggling in the wagon.

Half a block away sat Tad, still yelling on the ground.

"I *thought* the wagon felt a Tad lighter," said Abraham Lincoln.

On another night Abraham Lincoln invited people over.
His wife liked to have parties.
He told his boys to go to bed.

Tad liked parties too.
He climbed out of bed and tiptoed downstairs.
He didn't care that he was wearing a red nightgown.

Tad looked around at the ladies.
They wore bright dresses with hoopskirts.
The hoopskirts looked like colored mushroom tops.

The men wore long black coats.

Some smoked cigars that looked like little chimneys.

Tad spotted the dining room table.

It was covered with frosted cakes.

Tad thought he would have one.

Or two.

Or six.

Soon Tad wore a frosted chin.

People were watching him and laughing.

"Looks like someone has come to our party without an invitation."

Tad knew his father's voice.

"Back to bed, my fine frosted friend," said Abraham Lincoln.

The tall man lifted the boy into the air.
Tad squealed.
He wrapped his legs around Pa's neck.
It was the best place in the world to ride!

In 1860 Abraham Lincoln was elected President of the United States.
"We are going to the White House," he told Tad.
"You are going to have to be good there."
Tad nodded.
"I am *always* good," he fibbed.

# *Chapter Three*

Tad liked the White House.
It had giant rooms and long staircases.
It had long hallways and lots of closets.
There were so many places to hide.

There was only one thing wrong.
Pa was not around as much.
He was always having meetings.
Sometimes he was gone in the morning.
Sometimes he was gone in the afternoon.
Sometimes he was gone at night.

People, people, people!

They all came to the White House to see Pa.

One morning Tad woke up early.

He washed and dressed and ran downstairs.

"Would you like some breakfast?" asked the cook.

"I would like some string," said Tad.

The cook shook her head and smiled.

She knew Tad was probably up to no good.

"With milk?" she teased.

Tad shook his head and smiled.

"Nope. Just a long piece of string, please."

Now the cook was sure Tad was up to no good.
That's when he said "please" and "thank you."

Sure enough, Tad said "thank you" when
he got the string.
The cook shook her head as he left the kitchen.

Soon people arrived to see President Lincoln.
They found Tad at the bottom of the staircase.
He held a string across the stairs.

"One cent toll," the boy said.
He held out one of his father's long hats.

"This is something new," one red-headed
man blustered.
"I don't have one cent," another man flustered.

"Maybe you can borrow from someone," Tad suggested.
"If not, come back tomorrow.
Only members of the Lincoln family pass by for free."

Tad's mother shut down the stairway toll fast.
But not before the boy earned thirty cents.
It was enough to buy ice cream for his three brothers.
Tad ate the biggest scoops!

On another morning Tad found a mystery box.
It controlled the bells for the White House servants.

There were bells for maids.
There were bells for clerks.
There were bells for guards.
Tad rang every bell.

People came running from every direction.

"You rang for a maid?" one lady asked President Lincoln.
"What may I get for you?" a butler asked Mrs. Lincoln.
"You sent for the White House guards?" a man shouted.

President Lincoln just shook his head.
"Someone better find Tad.
This looks like the work of a White House wildcat I know."

# Chapter Four

Tad had a special gift.
He could always make President Lincoln laugh.
The man needed to laugh sometimes.
His years in the White House were sad times.
The country was at war.

Tad watched his father closely.
One morning the boy talked to his brothers
Willie and Robert.

"I think we should have a circus," Tad said.
"A circus!" Willie said.
"We have no animals!" said Robert.

"We can be the animals," declared Tad.

That afternoon the Lincoln Brothers Circus was held.
President Lincoln said he was too busy to leave
his office.

So the circus came to President Lincoln.

Tad was the ringmaster.
"Let me pre-sent. . ." the boy shouted.
". . .the wild monkeys of Africa!"

Willie and Robert dashed in.
They gobbled bananas and jumped up on the table.
The boys scratched under their arms and made
funny noises.
Tad joined them.

"And now . . ." yelled Tad.
". . . we have elephants from India."

Off the table the boys jumped.
They pulled long paper noses from under their shirts.
They hooked them around their ears.

Then they got down on their hands and knees.
Around the room the boys trotted.
They trumpeted like elephants.

"What is all this noise?"
Mrs. Lincoln stood in the doorway.

"Look at your sons," said President Lincoln.
"Oh, they are not *your* sons?" asked Mrs. Lincoln.

Tad smiled.
"We are the sons of elephants in India," he said.
Everyone in the room laughed loudly.

# *Chapter Five*

One December day Tad was walking behind
the White House.
Suddenly his eyes widened.
There stood a grand turkey inside a fence.

Quickly Tad ran forward.
"Who are you?" the boy asked.
"Where did you come from?"

"Some farmer sent him."
A White House worker fed the turkey some corn.
"The bird is for your family's Christmas dinner."

Every day Tad came to visit the turkey.
The boy called the bird Jack.
Jack danced and pranced around his pen.
He followed Tad around the White House yard.

Days slipped into weeks.

Soon Christmas was only one day away.

"The bird is good and fat," said the White House worker.

"He'll make a fine feast tomorrow."

Tad shook his head.

Jack would *not* make a fine feast tomorrow.

Quickly the boy ran into the White House.

He ran upstairs where his father was in a meeting.

"Pa, you can't have Jack killed!" Tad declared.
President Lincoln looked around at the other
people present.
"You all know my son Tad," said the older man.
"Now who is Jack?"

"Jack is my friend, Pa.
I know he's just a turkey.
But he's still my friend."

Lincoln looked down at his son.
"But he was sent here for our Christmas dinner."

"Pa, Jack is my friend.
He would be your friend too if you knew him.
Now which would you rather have. . ."
Tad stopped, looking up at his father.
". . .a good dinner or a good friend?"

President Lincoln rubbed his chin.
Then he turned and walked to his desk.
He took a piece of paper and a quill pen.
After inking the pen, he wrote:
JACK IS PARDONED.
He gave the note to Tad.

"Take this to the cook."

The President nodded his head.
"One good friend is worth a lifetime
of good dinners," he said.
Tad hugged his father.
"Thanks, Pa."

# Chapter Six

BOOM!

Tad sat up in bed.

Had he been dreaming?

CA-BOOM!

No, it was no dream.

Cannons were firing.

Tad jumped out of bed and ran to the window.

CA-BOOM! CA-BOOM!

Suddenly a door flew open.

"The war's over!" Robert cried.

"People are shooting the cannons to celebrate!"

Tad washed and dressed quickly.
He wanted to see his father.
For four long years the war had gone on.
Now it was over.

President Lincoln was in his office.
Tad ran in and hugged him.
"Oh, Pa, I'm so glad it's over."
Tad was twelve years old.
Some might have thought it foolish for a boy to act so.
But he didn't care.
And neither did Pa.

That day President Lincoln and Tad took a walk.
They went to have their picture taken.
"I believe I'll sit down for this," said the President.
"And I believe I'll stand up," said Tad.

President Lincoln picked up a book to hold.
Tad stood on his father's left.
The boy hooked his thumb into his pants' pocket.
It was just like his father often stood.

That night bands played on the White House lawn.
Rockets exploded overhead.
The people came to hear the President.
He stood on the balcony and read a speech.
"We must all work together now," said President Lincoln.
"We shall have a day of giving thanks that the war is over."

Tad held the candle to light the pages.
He took the pages of the speech as his father finished reading each one.
"I like what you said, Pa," the boy said.
"You made the people happy—and me too."

Three days later the happiness ended.
President Lincoln was shot and killed.
Tad Lincoln felt alone.

"I must learn to take care of myself," he said.
"I am only Tad Lincoln now, little Tad, like other little boys."

Tad left the White House and never returned.
But people still talk about him.
They remember him as the White House Wildcat.

And they remember him for making Abraham Lincoln laugh.

# *Bibliography*

Bayne, Julia Taft. *Tad Lincoln's Father*, Boston: Little, Brown & Company, 1931.

Carmer, Carl. *Pets at the White House*, New York: E. P. Dutton & Co., Inc., 1959.

Nolan, Jeanette Covert. *Abraham Lincoln*, New York: Julian Messner, Inc., 1953.

Sandburg, Carl. *Abraham Lincoln: The War Years*, (four volumes). New York: Harcourt, Brace and Company, 1939.

Weaver, John D. *Tad Lincoln: Mischief-Maker in the White House*, New York: Dodd, Mead & Company, 1963.

# About the Author

*"Why did I decide to write for children? Probably because some of my best childhood adventures I discovered in books. I have a great debt to repay. I owe so much to those wonderful authors who have brightened my life. Perhaps if I can be worthy of writing for young readers, part of my debt will be repaid."*

— David R. Collins

Today, David R. Collins is the author of over sixty books for children and youth. Not only that, he is in his 32nd year of teaching English in Moline, Illinois. The Illinois Office of Education has named him "Outstanding Educator," while the Illinois Veterans of Foreign Wars cited him as "Teacher of the Year" in 1988. He is the founder/director of both the annual Children's Literature Festival held in Moline and the

Mississippi Valley Writers Conference held at Augustina College in Rock Island, Illinois each year.

Collins received both his BS and MS Degrees from Western Illinois University. He has received numerous honors from his alma mater, including the Distinguished Alumni Award in 1993. Collins has also received recognition from the Junior Literary Guild. The American Freedom Foundation and U.N.E.S.C.O. In 1990, he was named winner of the Cornelia Meigs Award for outstanding juvenile writing.

Among junior writing circles, Collins has become known as "the king of children's biographies." Among his subjects have been Johnny Appleseed, Arthur Ashe, George Washington Carver, John Deere, Charles Dickens, Francis Scott Key, Abraham Lincoln, Charles Lindbergh, Florence Nightingale, Beatrix Potter, J. R. R. Tolkien, Harry S. Truman, Malcolm X, E.B. White, Woodrow Wilson, and many others.

"Young people are our most important readers," Collins concludes. "We who write for them must give them our best. What they read may leave a lasting impression. We want those impressions to offer direction, hope, and faith for the future."

# *About the Illustrator*

Leslie Carow Ossoff grew up in Walpole, Massachusetts. After high school she headed west to Colorado State University, where she majored in landscape architecture. After graduating in 1982, Leslie studied children's book illustration and graphic design at the Massachusetts College of Art and at the Manchester Institute of Arts and Sciences.

In addition to being an illustrator, Leslie is an avid cyclist. She has participated in races from 10 miles to 100 miles, and placed first in the Milbury Criterium and the New Hampshire Citizens Series in the late 1980s.

Leslie illustrated two other books for Discovery Enterprises, Ltd., *Lucretia Mott: Friend of Justice* and *Marjory Stoneman Douglas: Guardian of the Everglades*.

She and her husband David and their baby live in Concord, New Hampshire.

HOWELL-SOUTHEAST ELEMENTARY
35935 B LIN
Tad Lincoln : White House